555 TIMER

And Its Applications
(Second Revised & Updated Edition)

By

M.C. Sharma
M.Sc.

BPB PUBLICATIONS
B-14, CONNAUGHT PLACE, NEW DELHI-110001

LIMITS OF LIABILITY AND DISCLAIMER OF WARRANTY

Distributors:

COMPUTER BOOK CENTRE
12. Shrungar Shopping Centre,
M.G.Road, BENGALURU–560001
Ph: 25587923/25584641

DECCAN AGENCIES
4-3-329, Bank Street,
HYDERABAD-500195
Ph: 24756967/24756400

MICRO BOOKS
Shanti Niketan Building,
8, Camac Street, KOLKATA-700017
Ph: 22826518/22826519

BPB PUBLICATIONS
B-14, Connaught Place,
NEW DELHI-110001
Ph: 23325760/43526249

INFOTECH
Shop No. 2. F-38, South Extension Part-1
NEW DELHI-110049 Ph: 24691288

BPB BOOK CENTRE
376 Old Lajpat Rai Market,
DELHI-110006
Ph: 23861747

INFOTECH
G-2, Sidhartha Building,
96 Nehru Place, NEW DELHI-110019
Ph: 26438245

BUSINESS PROMOTION BUREAU
8/1 Ritchie Street, Mount Road,
CHENNAI-600002
Ph: 28410796/28550491

MICRO MEDIA
Shop No. 5, Mahendra Chambers,
150 DN Rd. Next to Capital Cinema,
V.T. (C.S.T.) Station,
MUMBAI-400 001
Ph: 22078296/2207829

Published by Manish Jain for BPB Publications, B-14, Connaught Place, New Delhi-110001 and Printed by him at Akash Press, New Delhi.

Contents

Measurement of Time 1
Timers 3
The Family of 555 Timers 21
Operation of 555 Type Timers 35
Practical Applications 43
    Testing 555 Type of Timer ICs 44
    Photo Timer 45
    Touch Plate Controller 46
    Auto Wiper Control 47
    Automatic Headlights Turn-Off 48
    Tiny Flasher 49
    Solid State Flasher 50
    Sense-of-Time Tester 51
    Audio Oscillator 52
    Square Wave Generator 53
    Square Wave Oscillator 54
    Linear Saw Tooth Generator 55
    Warble Tone Generator 57
    Delayed Automatic Power Off 58
    Delayed Automatic Power On 59
    Ni-Cd Battery Charger 60
    Wide Range Pulse Generator 61
    A Simple Tone Burst generator 63
    Frequency Divider 64
    Missing Pulse Detector 65
    Light Operated Relay 66
    DC-to-DC Converter 67
    Temperature Controller 68
    Brightness Control of LED Displays 69
    Long Duration Timer 70
    Sequential Switching 71
Appendix A 73
Index 75

Chapter One

Measurement of Time

Time is something that cannot be described in words. Ever since man started understanding time, all efforts were made to develop devices to measure time and display the time of the day. Sun dials were used during the day time and the positions of stars were used during night to know the time of the day.

When it was discovered that the time of swing of a pendulum depends only on its length, clocks using pendulums were developed These clocks used energy released by a falling weight or by the release of a wound spring, as the source of power and used pendulums to regulate time. A train of gears indicated time of the day by two hands on a dial. Figure 1.1 shows a weight operated grandfather type of clock and a wall clock using a wound spring.

Figure 1.1: A grandfather clock and a wall clock using pendulums.

Pendulum type of clocks were not portable because they had to be kept fixed at one place and set to operate in a vertical position only. Later on, a hair-spring and a balance-wheel combination was invented to regulate time. This invention resulted in development of portable timepieces, pocket watches and wrist watches. Some examples are shown in Figure 1.2.

Figure 1.2: An alarm time piece, a pocket watch and a wrist watch.

The time keeping accuracy of the above described time keeping devices was reasonably good, but not very accurate. Developments in the field of digital electronics resulted in highly accurate time keeping devices and time interval measurement devices. These devices displayed time directly in digits. A stop watch using hair spring and balance wheel combination, and an electronic digital stop watch are shown in Figure 1.3.

Figure 1.3: Analog and digital type of stop watches.

In course of time, the wound spring operated mechanism was replaced by an electric motor in some designs, while in others, the hair spring and balance wheel arrangement was designed to be maintained electronically. Such devices in which the action is continuous (like the unwinding of a wound spring, or rotation of an electric motor) are called *analog* devices.

In *digital* devices, the output waveform of a highly stable oscillator of precisely known frequency is converted into pulses and the time is measured by counting those pulses.

In this book we describe analog type of timers using the 555 IC family of timers. All types of timers, including digital timers, are described in author's book Electronic Timers and Practical Applications, published by BPB Publications.

Chapter Two

Timers

Timers are devices which, once started, stop automatically after the elapse of a prespecified time period, and give a visual or aural indication that the time is up. Examples of such timers are those used in some cooking appliances and therapy machines. In many designs, the timer, after the end of its timing cycle, generates a kind of output to initiate some action. For example, one timer in a washing machine triggers and starts another timer for next operation. In machines using compressors for refrigeration, timers are used to delay the start of the compressor motor after an interruption in the power supply.

Perhaps the first portable timer invented for wide usage was the sand clock timer shown in Figure 2.1. Here, fine sand filled in one pot escaped slowly through a narrow orifice to another pot below. Time was up when the pot on top became empty. This type of timer did not give any alarm when the time was up. Instead, someone had to keep a continuous watch to know when the time is up. The timer is restarted by turning the sand clock upside down. This type of timer was one of the first designs to keep time of the day. A watchman will ring a bell when the time was up and also restart the timer by turning it upside down.

Figure 2.1:
A sand clock
timer.

Basic Operation

A timer basically consists of a source of energy to power it, a time regulating element, a starting mechanism and a visual display or an aural indicator. In most cases, it also generates an output to initiate some action. Figure 2.2 shows the basic principle of operation of all kinds of timers.

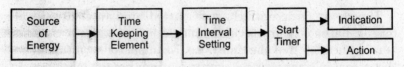

Figure 2.2: Basic elements of a timer.

The source of energy in mechanical timers, in most cases, is a spring which is wound tight by hand. The stored potential energy is released slowly. The rate of release is controlled by a time regulator mechanism, which can be a vibrating reed, or a hair spring and balance wheel type of arrangement used in mechanical time pieces. The main advantage of this arrangement is that no external power supply like a battery or mains supply is needed. Hence, such devices are portable, handy and economical to use. A dial on the face of the timer displays the time elapsed. In some designs, a sound is created by the timing mechanism to indicate that the timer is running. Time is up when the indicator hand returns to its zero mark, or when the sound stops. In some cases, an audio alarm powered by another spring is activated. Many designs close or open an electrical switch to control starting or stopping of an electrical appliance. For example, in therapy machines, the electrical power to the machine is cut off when the time is up. A typical mechanical timer is shown in Figure 2.2.

Figure 2.3:

A mechanical timer in which time is set by turning a knob.

In electromechanical timers, the source of energy is the mains supply and the time regulating mechanism is an electric motor. One example of such a timer which can directly be plugged into mains socket is shown in Figure 2.4.

Figure 2.4:

An electro-mechanical timer in which time is set by turning a knob.

Electronic Analog Timers

When transistors became available commercially, their small size and capability of operating at low voltages was immediately exploited to design simple and compact timers. These devices use the time taken by a capacitor to charge or discharge through a resistance from one voltage to another voltage, to measure the time interval. Let us have a look at the mathematical equations in the charge and discharge of a capacitor through a resistor.

Charging of a Capacitor

Figure 2.5 shows a capacitor C connected through a resistor R to a supply of voltage E. A push on the push-button switch Sw1 ensures that the initial voltage across the capacitor is zero. The moment Sw1 is opened, C starts charging through R, and the voltage V across the terminals of the capacitor starts rising. As the capacitor builds up charge, the voltage V developed across it opposes the input voltage E, and that reduces the effective charging voltage, and hence reduces the charging current. The rate of charging therefore becomes lesser and lesser. This is illustrated by a thick solid line curve in the time versus voltage graph in Figure 2.5. Theoretically, the voltage across the capacitor never reaches a value equal to E.

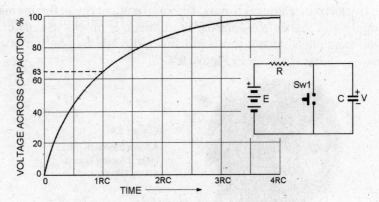

Figure 2.5: Charging of a capacitor through a resistor.

In practice, we are usually concerned by the time taken by the capacitor to charge from one voltage level, say V1, to another voltage level, say V2; or to discharge from a voltage level V2 to V1. In most practical cases, V1 and V2 are equal to one-third and two-third of the supply voltage.

The time taken by a capacitor to charge from voltage V1 to a voltage V2 (or to discharge from voltage V2 to voltage V1) can be calculated easily when we know the right equations.

The voltage V across the terminals of a charging capacitor after elapse of time 't' is given by the equation:

$$V = E (1 - e^{-t/RC}) \text{ ----------------------- (2-1)}$$

where E is the supply voltage, V is the voltage across the capacitor at any time 't' and 'e' is the natural number (2.718).

If t is taken to be equal to RC,

then $V = E (1 - e^{-1})$

or $V = E (1 - 1/e)$

or $V = E (1 - 1/2.718) = 0.632 E$

This implies that a capacitor charges to 63.2% of the supply voltage in a time equal to RC. This time RC is called the *time constant*, and is often denoted by the Greek letter τ (pronounced as tau).

If resistance R is in ohms and capacitance C is in Farads, time constant τ is in seconds. On the other hand, if R is in megohms and C is in microfarads, τ is again in seconds.

Equation 2-1 can be rewritten as:

$$V/E \quad = \quad 1 - e^{-t/RC},$$

or $\quad e^{-t/RC} \quad = \quad 1 - V/E \text{ - (2-2)}$

If we take V/E = 2/3, we get

$$e^{-t/RC} \quad = \quad 1-2/3 = 1/3 \quad = 0.3333$$

or $\quad -t/RC \quad = \quad \ln(0.3333) \quad = -1.098$

or $\quad t \quad = \quad 1.098RC \quad = 1.1\,RC \text{ - - - - - - - - (2-3)}$

This expression shows that the time taken by a capacitor to charge from zero to a voltage equal to two-third (66.67%) of the supply voltage is equal to 1.1 times the product of R and C. For example, a 5 microfarad capacitor charging from a battery of 12V through a 2 megohms resistor will take $1.1 \times 5 \times 2 = 11$ seconds to charge from zero to 8 volts.

It is interesting as well as important to note that the charging time *does not* depend on the value of the supply voltage. The capacitor-resistor combination will take exactly the same time to charge from zero to 40V if the supply voltage is raised to 60V. This fact is of great practical significance because it enables us to design simple timing circuits in which the time interval is not affected by variations in supply voltage.

Discharging of a Capacitor

Figure 2.6 shows a capacitor already charged to a voltage E. This capacitor can be connected to a resistance R by closing switch Sw1. As soon as the switch is closed, the capacitor starts discharging through resistor R.

As the capacitor discharges, the voltage E across it starts falling, and that reduces the discharging current. Theoretically, the capacitor will discharge to zero volts only after infinite time. The discharge curve of the capacitor is shown in Figure 2.6 by a thick line.

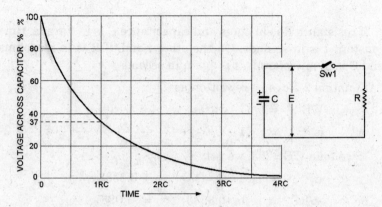

Figure 2.6: Discharging of a capacitor through a resistor.

The equation of discharge is:

$$V = E.e^{-t/RC} \text{ -} (2\text{-}4)$$

If t = RC, we get:

$$V \quad = \quad E.e^{-1}$$

or $V \quad = \quad E \times 1/2.718 \qquad = \quad 0.367$

This shows that the capacitor discharges to 36.7% of its initial voltage in t = RC seconds.

Equation 2-4 can be rewritten as:

$$V/E \qquad = \qquad e^{-t/RC}$$

or $e^{-t/RC} \qquad = \qquad V/E$

or $-t/RC \qquad = \qquad \ln(V/E)$

If we take V/E = 1/3, we get

$$e^{-t/RC} \qquad = \qquad 1/3 \qquad = 0.3333$$

or $-t/RC \qquad = \qquad \ln(0.3333) \quad = -1.098$

or $t \qquad = \qquad 1.098RC \qquad = 1.1\,RC \text{ - - - - - - -} (2\text{-}5)$

This expression shows that a charged capacitor will take a time interval t equal to 1.1RC to discharge from its initial voltage to one-third (33.3%) of that voltage. As before, this time interval is also independent of the supply voltage.

In many practical applications (e.g.; the design of RC oscillators) we are more concerned with the time taken by a capacitor to charge from V1 to V2 and then discharge from V2 to V1.

If V1 is equal to 1/3E and V2 is taken as 2/3E, the time 't' taken by a capacitor to charge from V1 to V2 is given by the expression:

$$
\begin{aligned}
t \quad &= \quad -[\ln (1/3)RC] - - [\ln (2/3)RC] \\
&= \quad -[-1.0986RC] - -[-0.4054RC] \\
&= \quad 0.693RC \quad \cong 0.7RC - - - - - - - - - - - (2\text{-}6)
\end{aligned}
$$

Similarly, the discharge time from V2 = 2/3E to V1 = 1/3E is also equal to 0.693RC, or approximately 0.7RC.

Effect of Capacitor Leakage

In all above calculations we have assumed that the capacitor is a perfect one in which the dielectric has no leakage. In practice, there is always some leakage, however small it may be. It usually increases with the value of capacitance. Practical electrolytic capacitors have more leakage than paper or mylar ones.

For understanding the effect of this leakage on the charging and discharging of capacitors, the leakage resistance can be shown as a resistance connected in parallel with the capacitor as shown in Figure 2.7 where R1 is the series resistance through which the capacitor charges, and R2 is the leakage resistance. The capacitor, in this case, is taken to be an ideal one with no leakage.

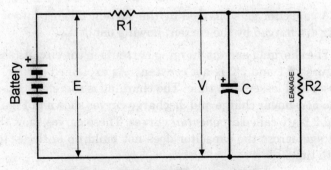

Figure 2.7: Effect of leakage on charging time.

Resistances R1 and R2 form a voltage divider and the voltage V available for the capacitor to charge is given by the equation

$$V = E \times R2/(R1+R2)$$

This voltage is always lower than battery voltage E. If R2 is comparable with R1, the capacitor may never charge to the expected voltage, say two-third of battery voltage. In practice, R2 should be at least ten times the value of R1. In other words, R1 should be not more than one-tenth of the expected value of R2 for the circuit to function properly.

Tantalum Capacitors

Tantalum electrolytic capacitors use solid electrolytes along with tantalum metal. They have much lower leakage than the usual aluminium types. This makes them eminently suitable for purposes such as signal coupling, timing circuits as well as filters in power supplies. The usual forms of these electrolytic capacitors are tubular axial types or miniature beads. Their voltage range is 6.3V to 35V, with capacitance values of 1.0 µF to 100 µF. Their temperature range is -55° C to +85° C.

Tantalum electrolytics can be used without any d.c. bias and can also accept a small reverse voltage, typically less than 1V. A minimum leakage current of 1µA is to be expected. Where longer time constants are needed, tantalum capacitors can be a better choice.

Constant Current Charging

A capacitor gets charged by the current flowing into it and it gets discharged by the current flowing out of it.

The charging and discharging currents in the circuits shown in Figures 2.1 and 2.2 is not constant. As explained earlier, it gets lesser and lesser with time. The charging is therefore, not linear. The non-linear charge and discharge curves shown in Figures 2.1 and 2.2 are called *exponential* curves. These curves show that the voltage across the capacitor does not build up or decay linearly with time.

The charge Q on a charging capacitor at any time is given by the equation:

$$Q = i \times t \quad \text{where } i \text{ is the current any t is the time.}$$

If current i is in amperes and time t is in seconds, then the charge Q is in coulombs.

The voltage V across a capacitor is given by the equation:

$$Q = C \times V \text{ -------------------------- (2-7)}$$

In this expression, if C is in farads and V is in volts, charge Q is in coulombs. The above equation can be written as:

$$V = Q/C$$
$$= it/C \text{ --------------------------- (2-8)}$$

This equation shows that if charging current i is kept constant, the voltage across a capacitor will build up linearly with time as shown by a graph in Figure 2.12.

Constant Current Sources

Circuits that deliver a constant current are called constant current sources and are denoted by the following symbol:

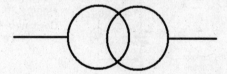

Figure 2.8: A symbol for representing a constant current source.

Constant current sources are sources of high voltages with very high internal resistance so that the output current is determined only by the internal resistance and is little affected by variations in load resistance. One illustrative circuit to explain the concept of a constant current source is shown in Figure 2.9. Here, a 100K resistance is connected in series with a battery of 100V. The load resistance (shown as 10K in this circuit) can be anything from 0 ohms to 10K. The current in the load resistance will remain the same (approximately 1 mA within 10%)..

An equivalent circuit is also shown on right in Figure 2.9.

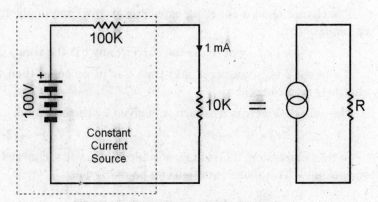

Figure 2.9: Illustrating a constant current source.

If the 10K load resistor is replaced by a capacitor as shown in Figure 2.10, the voltage across the capacitor will rise linearly with time up to a voltage of about 10V. The scale of the voltmeter can be directly marked in time units. After reaching about 10V, non-linearity sets in gradually.

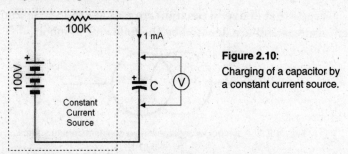

Figure 2.10:

Charging of a capacitor by a constant current source.

In practice, it is not always possible to use high voltage sources. Electronic circuits that operate at low voltages have been designed and used to simulate constant current sources.

The collector resistance of a transistor is very high. In other words, the collector current depends only on the base current and is affected very little by variations of its collector voltage. If the base current is kept constant, the collector current (and hence the emitter current) will remain almost constant for wide variations in load resistance. Two examples of constant current sources designed on this principle are shown in Figure 2.11.

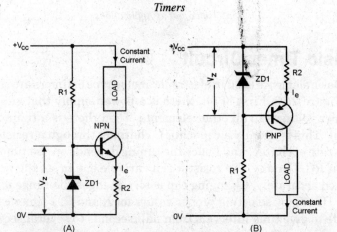

Figure 2.11: Constant current sources using

In Figure 2.11A, an n-p-n type of transistor is used as a constant current source. The base of this transistor is supplied with a fixed voltage as determined by the zener voltage of the zener diode ZD1. The emitter current, and hence the collector current also, stabilizes when the voltage drop across the emitter resistance R2 plus V_{be} of the transistor (about 0.7V for a silicon transistor) equals the zener voltage of the zener diode. The value of the constant current can be set by choosing R2. The constant current source at Figure 2.11B is very similar except that it uses a p-n-p transistor. The voltage across a capacitor charging through a constant current source rises linearly with time as shown in Figure 2.12

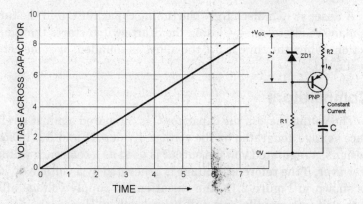

Figure 2.12: Linear charging of a capacitor.

Basic Timer Circuit

Basic elements used in electronic analog type of timers are shown in Figure 2.13. First of all, there is a power supply that supplies proper voltages to all other elements. Then there is a timing element. This is usually a capacitor C charging through a resistor R. The rate of charge, and hence the timing depends on the time constant RC. Usually, the resistor is a variable one to set the timer's period accurately. Changing capacitors changes the range of timing. Hence, by selecting proper values for R and C, a timer can be made to give time intervals from milliseconds to several seconds.

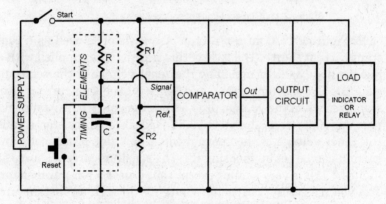

Figure 2.13: Basic circuit of analog timers.

A Reset switch discharges the timing capacitor C and the timer is made ready to start. Closing the Start switch starts the timing action. When the time is up, the alarm is sounded, or some action is started.

Comparators

The voltage across the capacitor C is compared against a reference voltage generated by the voltage divider R1 and R2. In some designs, a regulated voltage output is used as a reference voltage. However, if the reference voltage is generated by a voltage divider as shown in Figure 2.13, the variations in supply voltage affect both voltages equally and nullify each other. Hence, the timer's timing is not affected by variations in supply voltage.

The moment the voltage across the capacitor C rises above the reference voltage, the electronic comparator circuits generates an output. A simple comparator circuit using a single transistor and a fixed voltage for reference is shown in Figure 2.14.

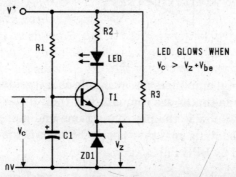

Figure 2.14: A simple comparator using a fixed reference voltage.

The emitter of the transistor is clamped at a fixed voltage V_z by a zener diode. If the input voltage (voltage V_c across the capacitor in this case) exceeds the zener voltage plus the base-emitter voltage drop V_{be} of the transistor (about 0.7V in the case of a silicon transistor), the transistor starts conducting and the LED glows.

A very important consideration in the design of comparator circuits is that the input impedance of the circuit should be very high. That is, they should not load the input circuit by drawing current from it. The first stage of the threshold detector circuit is therefore either an emitter follower, or it uses a MOS type of transistor. Since a single transistor amplifier cannot provide much gain, d.c. amplifiers containing many transistor amplifier stages are used. In practice, it is much more convenient to use a ready made integrated circuit which has all these features built in.

Figure 2.15 shows a comparator circuit using the popular 741 op amp. An op amp (operational amplifier) is a d.c. amplifier with very high gain and a high input impedance. It has two inputs that are marked (+) and (−). In Figure 2.15, if input V1 at the (+) input is slightly higher than V2 at the (−) input, the output will swing to fully high. If V1 is a little less than V2, the output goes low, to almost 0 volts.

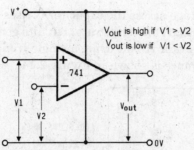

Figure 2.15:
A comparator circuit
using a 741 op amp.

Operational amplifiers are available as integrated circuits. The circuits inside the IC are complex, but their use is easy. All that you need to know is the pin connections and gain. Op amps are described in details in author's book OP Amps Made Simple, which is published by BPB Publications.

Hysteresis

The output of a comparator is either 'high' or 'low'. It is desirable that the transition from one state to another is fast and without any jitter or chatter. To understand the problem, let us have another look at Figure 2.14. Initially, when the voltage across the capacitor is less than the threshold (reference) voltage, transistor T1 is cut off and its base does not draw any current. The LED remains dark. When the voltage across the capacitor just reaches a little higher than the threshold voltage, the base of the transistor draws a small bias current and the LED is lit. But, as soon as the base and the load start drawing current, the voltage across the capacitor falls a little and LED is extinguished.

This goes on repeating and the output indicator LED will be on and off at a fast rate. If the load is a relay, it will chatter. The output jitter can be eliminated by separating the turn-on and turn-off voltages of the threshold detector by a finite amount.

For example, if the LED lights up when the capacitor voltage is 7 volts. Once lit, the LED should remain lit till this voltage falls below 5V. The LED should again light up when the voltage has risen to 7V. This difference between the turn-on and the turn-off voltages (2V in this case) is called hysteresis. In this case, the circuit has a hysteresis of 2V.

Time Up Indicators

This output of comparator is amplified and the amplified output is used to create an audio alarm, or a visual alarm to indicate that the time is up. In many cases, this output operates an electrical switch via a relay and that is used for control of heavier equipments or for initiating some action.

The low level output of the comparator can be directly used to give a visual or an aural indication if the input needed by the output indicator is small. Two such circuits are shown in **Figure 2.16**. Both circuits are RC oscillators in which the frequency is determined by the time constant R1 and C1.

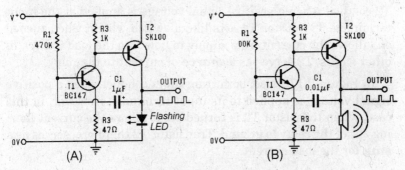

Figure 2.16: Time up indicators.

In the circuit shown in Figure 2.16A, R1 is 470K and C1 is 1 µf. The time constant is about 0.5 seconds and the LED therefore, flashes at about 2 times per second. In Figure 2.16B, the time constant is about 0.001 second and the loudspeaker produces a sharp tone, loud enough to attract attention.

Source Current or Sink Current

The amplified output is used to drive a load for indication or for initiating next action. Figure 2.17 shows two circuits in which the amplified output energizes a relay. These circuits show a relay with one contact only, but a relay with many contact pairs can be used as well Separate contacts can be used for different **purposes**. Relays of all types are described in details in author's book **Relays and Their Applications**, published by BPB Publications.

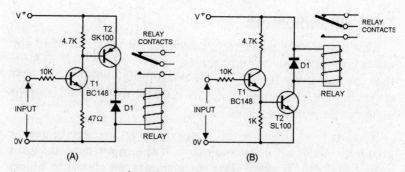

Figure 2.17: Load drivers.

In the circuit shown at Figure 2.17A, both transistors T1 and T2 conduct when a positive signal voltage is applied at the input terminals. Transistor T2 acts like a switch which, when turned on, allows the current from supply to flow into the load (relay). In other words, T2 serves as a **source** of current to the relay.

In Figure 2.17B also, both transistors conduct when a positive signal voltage is applied to its input terminals. However, in this case, when transistor T2 is turned on, it allows the current flowing out of the relay to ground. Transistor T2 therefore, serves as a **sink** for the load current.

Driving Inductive Loads

In Figure 2.17, the output transistor is used to drive a relay. A relay or a contactor forms an inductive load. If the current flowing in an inductive load is suddenly turned off, a large voltage of reverse polarity is produced across the inductive load terminals because of self induction. This high back e.m.f. can puncture the junctions of the driving transistor and render them inoperative. A simple technique used to overcome this problem is to connect a diode across the load terminals with reverse polarity as shown in Figure 2.17. This diode does not draw any current during normal operation, but it acts as a short circuit for the reverse polarity voltage generated due to self induction, and absorbs all its power. This ensures safety to the driving transistor. Some designers prefer to keep this diode in series with the inductive load. A capacitor is sometimes used in parallel with the relay for the same purpose.

Totem Pole Outputs

Some integrated circuits have an output of the type which can either source or sink output current. Such output stages are called as totem-pole outputs. It is necessary to understand their working before using them in practical applications. A simple circuit of such an output stage is shown in Figure 2.18 to explain its working.

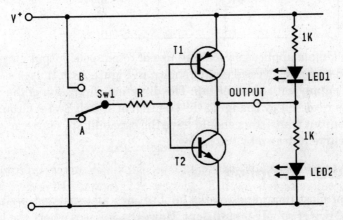

Figure 2.18: Totem-pole output.

The circuit uses a pair of complementary transistors. One p-n-p transistor T1 and one n-p-n transistor T2 are connected in series. Their bases are joined and the junction can be connected either to the positive supply line, or to ground by a single-pole two-way switch Sw1.

When the switch is put in position A as shown in Figure 2.18, transistor T2 is fully cutoff and transistor T1 is fully conducting. The output is therefore approximately equal to the supply voltage and LED2 lights up. LED1 remains dark. In other words, the circuit works as a **source** of supply of current to LED2.

When Sw1 is thrown to position B, transistor T1 gets cutoff and transistor T2 becomes fully conducting. In this case, LED1 lights up and LED2 goes off. In this state, the current from the supply line to light up LED1 is sunk to ground through T2. The circuit therefore, works as a current **sink** for the load current.

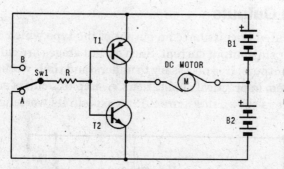

Figure 2.19:
A simple motor reversal circuit.

A simple application making use of totem pole output stage is the d.c. motor reversal circuit shown in Figure 2.19. It uses a battery supply with a center tap. The direction of rotation of the motor is reversed by changing the position of switch Sw1. Of course, the output transistors should have the capability to source or sink the current drawn by the motor.

Power Supplies

For most timer and related applications, unregulated, well-filtered power supply is sufficient. However, in cases where the load draws heavy current, chatter may be experienced. This is because the output of an unregulated supply drops a little when a load is applied. This drop in voltage can change the threshold voltage which turns off the load current. But, as soon as the load is turned off, the power supply output rises and the load is energized again. This can result in chattering of a relay, or unstable operation. The remedy is to isolate the two supplies as shown in Figure 2.20. Power supplies of all kinds are described in details in author's book **Power Supplies for All Occasions**, published by BPB Publications.

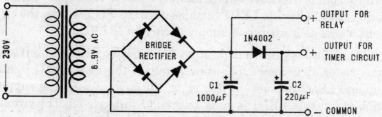

Figure 2.20: A simple power supply for timer applications.

Chapter Three

The Family of 555 Timers

The 555 timer integrated circuit was introduced in 1972. It soon became very popular because of its versatility. Several models and versions were introduced subsequently. We describe their characteristics in this chapter.

The 555 Timer

Basically, the 555 timer is a highly versatile integrated circuit capable of generating fairly accurate and stable time delays. Circuit design using a 555 timer IC requires minimum number of components. The circuit can be triggered and reset on falling edge of waveforms. Its prominent features are:

- Timing from milliseconds to hours
- Monostable and astable operation
- Adjustable duty cycle
- Ability to operate from a wide range of supply voltages
- Output compatible with CMOS, DDL. TTL
- High current output that can source or sink 200 mA
- Trigger and reset inputs are logic compatible
- Output can be operated normal ON and normal OFF
- High temperature stability

The 555 timer is available in an 8-pin and a 14-pin dual-in-line packages, or in a circular TO-99 metal can with eight leads. Pin connections for these packages are shown in Figure 3.1.

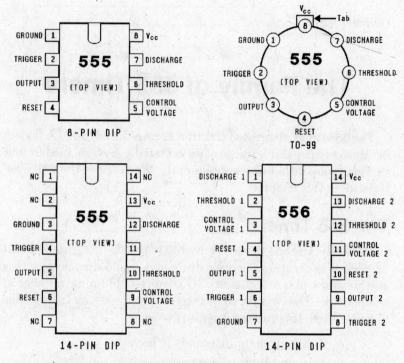

Figure 3.1: Pin connections of 555 and 556 timers (Top Views).

The SE and NE versions are similar except for maximum temperature ratings. The precision type SE maintains its essential characteristics over a temperature range of -55° to +125°C while the general purpose type NE operates reliably only over a range of 0°C to 70°C. Some manufactures use the suffix C to indicate the commercial version for general purpose applications. Both types have a maximum rating of 18 volts and can handle power dissipation of up to 600 mW.

The inside circuitry of a 555 timer is shown in Figure 3.2. Comprising of 23 transistors, 2 diodes and 16 resistors, the 555 has built-in compensation for component tolerance and temperature drift resulting in a temperature coefficient of only 25 parts per million per degree Centigrade. A functional block diagram of 555 timer is shown in Figure 3.3.

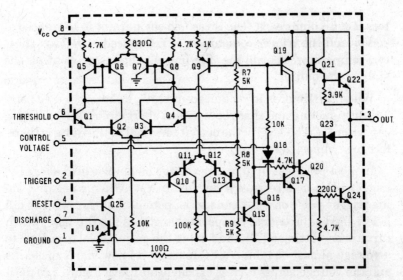

Figure 3.2: Schematic diagram of 555 timer.

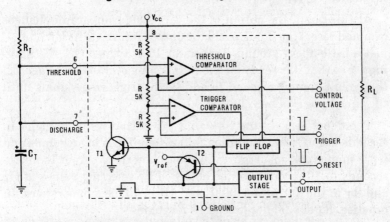

Figure 3.3: A functional block diagram of 555 timer.

Operation

As shown in Figure 3.3, the 555 timer consists of two comparators, two control transistors, a flip-flop and buffered output stage. The reference voltages for the two comparators inside the IC are developed across a voltage divider consisting of three equal resistors R of 5K ohms each. The threshold comparator is referenced at $2/3V_{cc}$ and the trigger comparator is referenced at $1/3V_{cc}$. These two comparators control the [1]flip-flop which, in turn, controls the state of the output.

When the timer is in its quiescent state, its internal transistor T1 is conducting and that represents a short circuit across timing capacitor C_T. The level of the output terminal in this state is therefore low, almost zero.

In most practical circuits, the voltage on pin 2 is held above the trigger point by a resistor connected to V_{cc}. When a negative-going trigger pulse on pin 2 causes the potential at this point to fall below $1/3V_{cc}$ the trigger comparator switches the flip-flop[1], which turns over, cutting off T1 and forcing the output level to go high to a voltage almost equal to V_{cc}. Capacitor C_T now starts to charge and the voltage across it rises exponentially (see Figure 2.5) until it reaches $2/3V_{cc}$.

At this point, the output of the threshold comparator changes over and resets the flip-flop and the output returns to its low state— just a little above ground. Transistor T1 is turned ON, discharging C_T so that it is ready for the next timing cycle. Once triggered, the circuit cannot respond to additional triggering signals until the timed interval has elapsed.

The delay period—the time that the output remains high—in seconds is $1.1C_TR_T$, (Equation 2-3) where R_T is in megohms and C_T is in microfarads. Figure 3.4 shows how delays from 10 microseconds to 10 seconds can be obtained by selecting values of C_T and R_T in the .001µF to 100µF and 1K to 10 megohms ranges. In practice, R_T should not exceed 10 megohms.

---

[1] A flip-flop functions like a toggle switch, which, when placed in one position remains in that position until its position is changed. The difference is that the change of state in a toggle switch is caused by a mechanical action, whereas in a flip-flop, it is caused by a trigger signal. Flip-flops are available as integrated circuits for independent applications. They are described in details in author's book Learning by Experiments — Digital Integrated Circuits, published by BPB Publications.

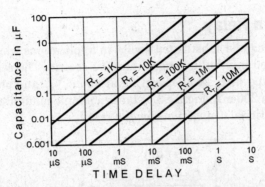

Figure 3.4: Delay times for different values of capacitors and resistors.

An important feature to be noted here is that 555, unlike many RC timers, provides a timed interval that is virtually independent of supply voltage V_{cc}. This is because the charge rate of C_T and the reference voltages to the threshold comparator and trigger comparator are all directly proportional to the supply voltage. Operating voltage can range from 4.5 volts to a maximum of 18 volts.

Feeding the Load

We have seen how the timed interval or delay is obtained. Now let us see how we can use it. A look at the output circuit (Q17 and Q19 in Figure 3.2) shows it to be a quasi-complementary transformerless arrangement (see Figure 2.18), similar to many audio output stages. Furthermore, we know that in this type of circuit, one side of the load goes to the emitter-collector junction of the output transistors and the other side of the load can be connected either to Vcc or to ground. The same applies to the load connected to the 555. Output pulses developed across load R_L can be obtained directly from pin 3.

When the load is connected to Vcc, a considerable amount of current flows through the load into terminal 3 when the output is low. When the output is high, the current through the load is quite small. Conditions are reversed when the load is returned to ground. The maximum current at terminal 3 is 200 mA when it is used as a current source or as a current sink.

Driving a Relay

A relay can be substituted for R_L in applications where the delay or timed interval is longer than 0.1 second. The relay should be a DC type with a coil operating at about V_{cc} and not drawing more than 200 mA. Figure 3.5 shows a simple manual timer with the two optional connections for the relay.

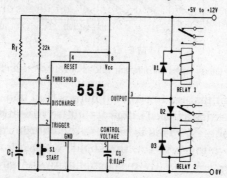

Figure 3.5: Driving an inductive load such as a relay.

You must be careful when connecting an inductive load such as a relay to the output of the 555 IC or any other solid-state device. This is because when the current flowing through an inductive load is interrupted, the collapsing magnetic field generates a high reverse emf (transient voltage) that can damage the device. The solution to this problem is to connect a diode (D1 or D3 in Figure 3.5) across the relay coil so that it conducts and absorbs the reverse voltage transient.

When the output at the output terminal (pin 3) is low, its voltage may not fall to zero. A small voltage available at the output may drive sufficient current to keep an energized relay latched on even when the output has fallen to low. The remedy is to connect a diode in series, like the diode D2 shown in Figure 3.5. The voltage drop inside this diode (0.7V for a silicon diode) will reduce the voltage available to the relay to almost zero and it will be released when the output falls to a low value. Relays of all types are described in author's book **Relays and Their Applications**, published by BPB Publications.

Triggering

As stated earlier, in most practical circuits, the trigger terminal is generally returned to V_{cc} through a resistor of about 22kΩ. However, the simplest method of triggering a 555 is to momentarily ground the terminal. This is OK as long as the ground is removed before the end of the timed interval. Thus, if the circuit shown in Figure 3.5 is used in an application like a photo-timer, tapping push button S1 is sufficient to trigger the circuit and start the timer.

In many applications, the 555 must be triggered by a pulse. The amplitude and minimum pulse width required for triggering are dependent on temperature and supply voltage. Generally, the current required for triggering is about 0.5 μA for a period of 0.1 μs. Triggering-voltage ranges from 1.67 volts when V_{cc} is 5 volts to 5 volts when V_{cc} is 15 volts.

Resetting

Once a timed cycle has been initiated by a negative-going pulse on pin 2, the circuit is immune to further triggering until the cycle has been completed. However, the timed cycle can be interrupted by grounding the reset terminal (pin 4) or applying a negative-going reset pulse to it. The reset pulse causes timing capacitor C_T to be discharged and forces the output to return to its quiescent low state. Reset voltage is typically 0.7 volt (or lower) and reset current is 0.1 mA. When the reset terminal is not being used, it should be connected to V_{cc} either directly or through a resistor.

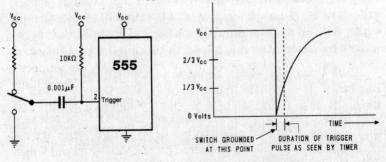

Figure 3.6: Creating a trigger pulse for a 555 timer.

If the timer is used for creating small time delays, triggering by hand is too slow for that purpose. The timer may get triggered again before the manually operated switch is released. A down going short-duration pulse is needed instead. This type of pulse can be generated by a 555 timer or any other electronic circuit. A circuit that generates a sharp and negative going triggering pulse by a push on a switch is shown in Figure 3.6.

The Control Terminal

The $2/3 V_{cc}$ point on the internal voltage divider is brought out to the control terminal (pin 5). The timing cycle can be modified by applying an external DC control voltage to pin 5. This permits manual or electronic remote control of the timed interval. The control terminal is seldom used when the timer is operated in the monostable mode and should be grounded through a 0.01µF capacitor to prevent the timed interval from being affected by pickup of a stray AC or RF signal.

When the timer is operated as an oscillator in the astable mode, the generated signal can be frequency modulated or pulse width modulated by applying a variable DC control voltage to pin 5.

False Triggering Prevention

Normally the Reset input (pin 4) is directly connected to the positive supply line. In that case, as soon as the power is switched on, the timer can get triggered and settles down only after completion of its timing cycle. This happens because the timing capacitor C_T is initially discharged and the Trigger input (pin 2) sees a low. This first time triggering is not objectionable in many applications. But in some applications where it is objectionable, some means for preventing this false triggering must be adopted.

If the timer circuit can be made to hold till the voltage on C_T has built up to a little higher than $1/3 V_{cc}$, the timer will work normally even from the start. Figure 3.7 shows a modified timer circuit. Here, the Reset input is held low for a period determined by the time constant R1C1. If this time is sufficient, false triggering will be eliminated.

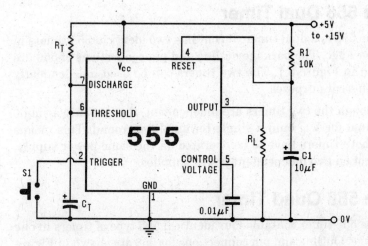

Figure 3.7: False trigger prevention.

It is easy to see that as the value of the timing capacitor C_T increases, the value of C1 should also be increased accordingly.

Output Surge

The 555 briefly draws a fairly high current when its output changes from low to high. This is so because Q24 (see Figure 3.2) is briefly driven into saturation, and it takes a while to actually turn off. This is a characteristic of bipolar transistors.

As soon as Q21 and Q22 conduct, a short, non-current-limited, short-circuit of the supply for a very short time arises because Q24 is still conducting. This current surge lasts for a very short time. It is for this reason that the 555 requires particular attention to be paid to decoupling of the supply voltage. Output switching from high to low causes fewer problems because Q21 and Q22 are not driven into saturation; hence the switch-off time is short relative to that of Q24. CMOS versions of the 555 generally do not suffer from this annoying effect.

The CMOS versions do not suffer the large peak current at output switch-over (described above), while the input bias current of the threshold comparator, and the leakage current of the discharge transistor, are also significantly reduced.

The 556 Dual Timer

The 556 is a dual timer. It contains two identical 555 timers in one package. The package outline and pin connections of 556 are shown in Figure 3.1. The two timers can be used independently for different purposes.

Though the two timers are independent, there is only a single terminal for V_{cc} and a single terminal for ground. This means that both timers have to be operated on the same power supply, and not on two independent power supplies.

The 558 Quad Timer

The 558 timer contains four identical 555 type of timers in one package. Outline and pin connections for 558 are shown in Figure 3.8, and its equivalent circuit is shown in Figure 3.9.

As it was in the case of a 556 dual timer, here also, there is one terminal for V_{cc} and one for ground. Hence, the timers have to be operated on a single common power supply. In addition, the 558 has single terminals for Control Voltage and for Reset.

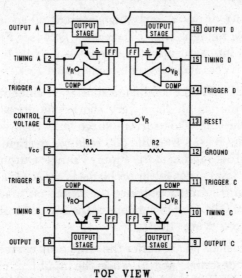

TOP VIEW

Figure 3.8: Pin connections of a 558 quad timer

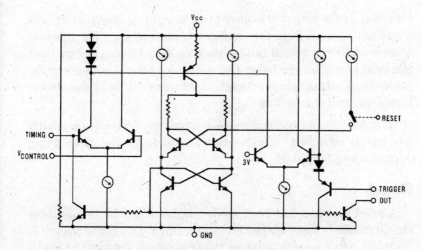

Figure 3.9: Equivalent circuit of a 558 quad timer.

Features

♦ 100 mA output current per section

♦ Edge triggered (no coupling capacitor needed)

♦ Output independent of trigger conditions

♦ Wide supply voltage range - 4.5 V to 16 V

♦ Time period equals RC

Applications

♦ Sequential timing

♦ Time delay generation

♦ Industrial controls

♦ Precision timing

♦ Quad one-shot

Output

As you can see in Figure 3.9, the 558 structure output is open collector. This implies that it can serve only as a sink for the load current. The load has to be connected between V_{cc} and output terminal. If the output is to be applied to another stage, it requires a *pull-up* resistor from the output terminal to V_{cc}. The internal transistor for the output is capable of sinking 100 mA per unit but the total power dissipated in the transistor should not exceed the power dissipation and junction temperature rating of the output transistor and the package.

As with 555 and 556 timers, the output in 558 is also normally low and is switched to high when triggered by the down going edge of a trigger pulse.

Reset

A reset function has been made available to reset all sections simultaneously to an output low state. During reset the trigger is disabled. After reset is finished, the trigger voltage must be taken high and then low to implement triggering. The reset voltage must be brought below 0.8 V to insure reset.

The Control Voltage

The control voltage is also made available on the 558 timer. It is applied to all the timers. The control voltage allows the threshold voltage to be modulated, thereby controlling the output pulse width and duty with an external control voltage. The range of this control voltage is from about 0.5 V to V_{cc} minus 1 volt. This will give a cycle time variation of about 50:1. In a sequential timer with voltage controlled cycle time, the timing periods remain proportional over the adjustment range.

The 7555 CMOS Timer

The power consumed by any circuit becomes an important consideration when the device has to be operated on batteries. The 555 timer uses bipolar type of transistors. Hence its power consumption is a little on the high side for battery operated applications. The 7555 is a CMOS version of the 555. A similar IC by Texas Instruments is TLC555. These devices are pin compatible with the bipolar 555. Figure 3.10 shows internal structure of a CMOS version of 555.

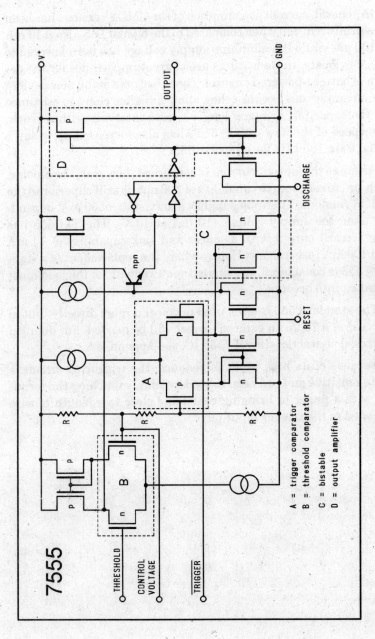

Figure 3.10: Internal structure of a CMOS version of 7555.

7555

THRESHOLD

CONTROL VOLTAGE

TRIGGER

V+

OUTPUT

GND

DISCHARGE

RESET

A = trigger comparator
B = threshold comparator
C = bistable
D = output amplifier

In general, current consumption of the CMOS versions has been drastically reduced when compared to the bipolar 555 – from 10 mA to 100 μA, while the minimum supply voltage has been lowered to 2 V. Obviously, these features are of great importance for the design of battery-powered circuits. These features of the new devices are advantageous because they allow a higher charge resistance for the capacitor, bringing longer timing intervals within reach. The speed of the new CMOS 555's has also increased up to say 1 MHz, from 180 kHz for a bipolar 555.

As far as the output current is concerned, however, the bipolar, with its current source capability of 200 mA, is still superior to the CMOS versions. The 7555 supplies a maximum of 50 mA, depending upon the supply voltage (10 mA at 10 V). The TLC555 has symmetrical output with a source and sink capability of 10 mA and 100 mA respectively. Hence, where the replacement of a standard 555 is considered, the current requirements of the load must be taken into account.

The standard 555 is often used to power a relay directly. But in the case of a 7555, an external driver will be needed. For detailed electrical characteristics of 7555 IC, see Appendix A.

Because of its high input impedance, the triggering circuit is quite sensitive and can be activated by simply touching the terminal with a finger or bringing your hand close to a length of wire fastened to the trigger input pin.

Chapter Four

Operation of 555 Type Timers

After knowing the basic characteristics of the timers available in the family of 555 timers, let us see the make-up and operation of the 555 IC and see how its various features can be developed into practical circuits.

Monostable Operation

All timer circuits are basically monostable or one-shot circuits which, once triggered, complete the timing cycle and wait for the next trigger to start the timing cycle again. Details of the external connections are shown in Figure 4.1. Waveforms showing the timing action and time relationship between the trigger and output are also shown on the right in Figure 4.1.

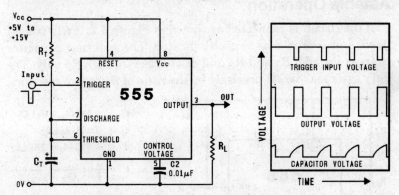

Figure 4.1: Monostable operation of a 555 timer.

The external timing capacitor C_T is held initially discharged by internal transistor T1 (see Figure 3.3). Upon application of a negative pulse to pin 2, the flip-flop is set which releases the short circuit across the external capacitor and drives the output high.

The voltage across the capacitor, now, rises exponentially with the time constant $R_T C_T$. When the voltage across the capacitor equals $2/3 V_{CC}$, the threshold comparator resets the flip-flop which, in turn, discharges the capacitor rapidly and drives the output to its low state. The circuit rests in this state till the arrival of the next pulse.

The circuit triggers on a negative going input signal when the level reaches below $1/3 V_{CC}$. Once triggered, the circuit will remain in that state until the set time is elapsed, even if it is triggered again during this interval. The time 't' that the output is in its high state is given by $t = 1.1 R_T C_T$.

Applying a negative pulse simultaneously to the Reset terminal (pin 4) and the trigger terminal (pin 2) during the timing cycle discharges the external capacitor C_T and causes the cycle to start over again. The timing cycle will now commence on the positive edge of the Reset pulse. During the time the reset pulse is applied, the output is driven to its low state. When the reset function is not in use, it is recommended that it be connected to V_{CC} to avoid any possibility of false triggering.

Astable Operation

If the circuit is connected as shown in Figure 4.2, it will trigger itself and free run as a multivibrator. The external capacitor charges through R_A and R_B and discharges through R_B only. The duty cycle may be set precisely by the ratio of these two resistors.

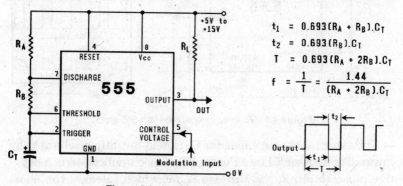

$$t_1 = 0.693(R_A + R_B).C_T$$
$$t_2 = 0.693(R_B).C_T$$
$$T = 0.693(R_A + 2R_B).C_T$$
$$f = \frac{1}{T} = \frac{1.44}{(R_A + 2R_B).C_T}$$

Figure 4.2: Astable operation of 555 timer.

In this mode of operation, the capacitor charges and discharges between $1/3V_{CC}$ and $2/3V_{CC}$. As in the triggered mode, the charge and discharge times, and hence the frequency is independent of the supply voltage.

The charge time (output high) is given by:

$$t_1 = 0.693 \, (R_A + R_B) \, C_T$$

The discharge time (output low) is given by:

$$t_2 = 0.693 \, (R_B) \, C_T$$

Thus the total period T is given by:

$$T = t_1 + t_2 = 0.693 \, (R_A + 2R_B) \, C_T \text{----------------(4-1)}$$

and the frequency of oscillation is then:

$$f = 1/T = 1.44 \, / \, [(R_A + R_B) \, C_T \text{----------------(4-2)}$$

This may be easily found by graph shown in Figure 4.3.

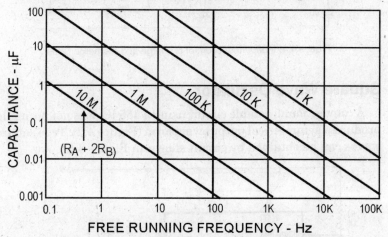

Figure 4.3: Free running frequency of astable multivibrator.

The duty cycle D is given by:

$$D = R_B \, / \, (R_A + 2R_B) \text{-------------------------(4-3)}$$

From the above equation, it will be seen that the frequency and the duty cycle are inter-dependent and change of value of R_A or R_B affects both.

It is possible to have a completely independent control of the charge and discharge times by using two external diodes as shown in Figure 4.4. The timing capacitor C1 charges through D1 and R1 and discharges through D2 and R2. A modified arrangement shown separately at left in Figure 4.4 provides a control over duty cycle without changing the output pulse frequency. The diode voltage drops, however, make the frequency, more sensitive to supply voltage variation.

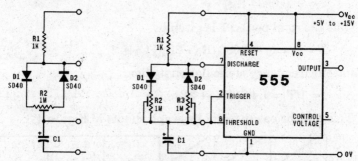

Figure 4.4: Independent control of charge and discharge times.

Square Wave Oscillator

A conventional astable circuit using a 555 IC does not normally produce a symmetrical output waveform (Figure 4.2). True square waves can be obtained by circuit shown in Figure 4.5.

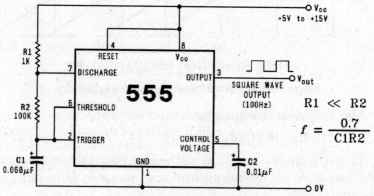

$$R1 \ll R2$$

$$f = \frac{0.7}{C1R2}$$

Figure 4.5: Square wave oscillator.

The asymmetry of a conventional astable circuit is a result of the fact that charging and discharging times are not equal. In Figure 4.5, capacitor C1 is charged through R1 and R2 while discharged through R2. If R1 is made very small compared to R2, then both time constants will be reduced so that they essentially depend on R2 and C1. The frequency of operation f is approximately equal to 0.7/(R2C1). The frequency is, of course, independent of the supply voltage.

Bistable Operation

As explained earlier, a flip-flop is a circuit that behaves like a change-over switch. It has two stable positions, and stays in any one position till made to change over. The 555 timer can also function as bistable flip-flop in such applications as TTL compatible drivers. This flip-flop offers the advantage that it operates from a range of supply voltages, uses little power and requires no external components other than bypass capacitors in noisy environments. It also provides a direct relay driving capability.

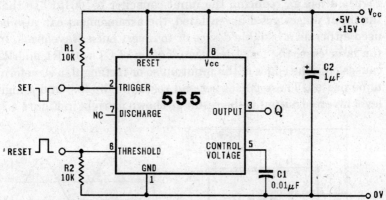

Figure 4.6: 555 Timer operated as a flip-flop.

As shown in Figure 4.6, a negative pulse applied to the trigger input terminal (pin2) sets the flip-flop and the output Q goes high. A positive going pulse applied to threshold terminal will reset the flip-flop and drive the output low. The flip-flop can also be reset by applying a negative going pulse to the Reset terminal (pin 4). In this mode pin 6 is normally kept low.

Schmitt Trigger

Apart from timing functions, the two comparators of the 555 timer can be used independently for other applications. One example is a Schmitt trigger shown in Figure 4.8. The two comparator inputs (pin 2 and 6) are tied together and biased at $1/2V_{CC}$ through a voltage divider R1 and R2. Since the threshold comparator will trip at $2/3 V_{CC}$ and the trigger comparator will trip at $2/3 V_{CC}$, the bias provided by the resistors R1 and R2 is centered within the comparators' trip limits.

A sine wave input of sufficient amplitude to exceed the reference levels causes the internal flip-flop to be set and reset. In this way, it creates a square wave at the output. So long as R1 is equal to R2, the 555 will be automatically biased correctly for almost any supply voltage. The output waveform is 180° out of phase with the applied sine wave. The circuit can be used as a signal shaper/buffer with advantage of availability of high output current.

By modifying the input time constant of the circuit shown in Figure 4.7 (e.g., reducing the input capacitor to .001μF) so that the input pulses get differentiated, the arrangement can also be used either as a bistable device or to invert pulse waveforms. In the later case, the fast time combination of C1 with R1 and R2 causes only the edges of the input pulse or rectangular waveform to be passed. These pulses set and reset the flip-flop and a high level inverted output is the result as shown on right in Figure 4.7.

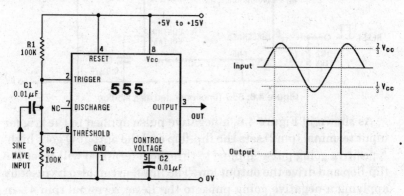

Figure 4.7: 555 Timer used as a Schmitt trigger.

Using Quad Timer 558

The 558 IC contains four similar timer circuits in one package. Each timer can be triggered by a down-going edge of the trigger pulse. This has the advantage that you don't have to use a coupling capacitor (see Figure 3.6) to trigger it. Its operation in different modes is described below:

Monostable or One-Shot operation

In the one shot mode of operation shown in Figure 4.8, it is necessary to supply a minimum of two external components, the resistor and capacitor for timing.

Unlike the 555, the time period in a 558 is equal to the product of R_T and C_T. An output load must be present between V_{cc} and the output terminal to complete the circuit of the open collector transistor. For this reason, R_L has been connected in Figure 4.8

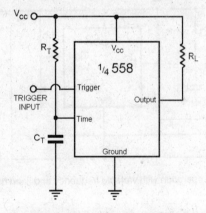

Figure 4.8: Using 558 as a one-shot.

Astable Operation

For astable operation, the outputs of two quads are direct coupled to the opposite trigger input. This circuit arrangement is shown in Figure 4.9.

The duty cycle can be set by ratio of R1C1 to R2C2 from close to zero to almost 100%.

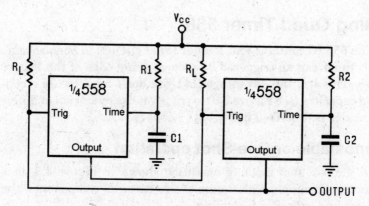

Figure 4.9: Astable multivibrator using two timers in a 558.

An astable circuit in which the frequency can be varied but the duty cycle is fixed is shown in Figure 4.10

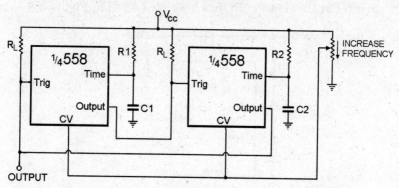

Figure 4.10: Astable operation with variable frequency and fixed duty cycle.

Chapter 5

Practical
Applications

After learning about the make-up and operation of the 555 ICs,
let us see how its various features can be developed into practical
circuits. This section describes a few simple types of applications.
They fully illustrate the power of the family of the 555 timer ICs.
After understanding the working of these applications, you can
modify them and design circuits for use in your own applications.

The values and ratings of components used are shown in the
Figures. All resistors, unless otherwise specified, are ¼W type.
Most of the components used are non-critical and can be replaced
by approximately equivalent components available readily.

Testing 555 Type of Timer ICs

In practical work, it is a frequent requirement to find out whether a particular timer IC is OK or not. A very simple circuit to make this kind of test is shown in Figure 5.1. Though the circuit shown is for a 555 IC, it can be applied to other ICs in the family as well.

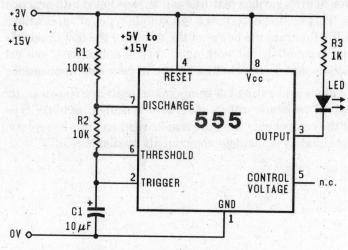

Figure 5.1: A simple tester for 555 type of ICs.

Basically, the tester circuit is an astable multivbrator of the type shown in Figure 4.2. In this case, the output is high for a time period equal to 1.1(R1+R2)C1 and the output is low for a time period equal to 1.1R2C1. Hence, the LED remains lit for a shorter period than the period for which it is off. In other words, the LED flashes at a slow rate. This flashing of LED is a sure test that the IC is OK.

The advantage of this circuit is that it needs very few external components and works on a supply of 3V to 15V. It is recommended that you use a socket for this circuit so that you do not have to solder connections to the IC to be tested.

Photo Timer

The circuit shown in Figure 5.2 is useful for providing controlled 'on' times for such equipment as photo-enlargers, developers, small heaters, incandescent lamps, etc. Time is set by potentiometer R2 which provides a range of 1 sec. to 100 seconds with timing capacitor C1 of 100 μF.

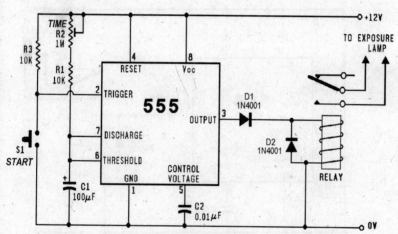

Figure 5.2: Photo Timer.

The output at pin 3 is normally low and the relay is held off. A momentary push on switch S1 energies the relay which is held closed for a time 1.1(R1+R2).C1 and then released. The exact length of the timing interval will depend on the actual capacitance of C1. Most electrolytic capacitors are rated on the basis of minimum guaranteed value and the actual value may be higher. The circuit should be calibrated for various positions of the control knob of R2 after the timing capacitor has had a chance to age. Once the capacitor has reached its stable value, the timings provided should be well within the photographic requirements.

Touch Plate Controller

Touch the small plate and the relay gets energized, kept on for about 100 seconds and then released. Such circuits are ideally suited for making touch-operated call-bells, buzzers or small toys which, once touched, operate for a small time and then switch off automatically.

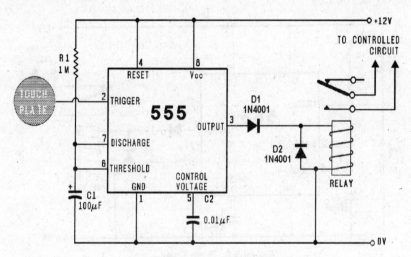

Figure 5.3: Touch controlled relay.

The input impedance of the trigger comparator of 555 is very high and hence, the circuit can be triggered by the ac and other voltage induced in a human body. This fact is used in making the touch switch shown in Figure 5.3. Toy motors can be driven directly by deleting the diodes D1, D2 and using a driver transistor.

Since the input impedances of CMOS circuits is much higher, touch circuits work better with CMOS ICs. A 7555 can be a good choice, but the output driving power requirements must be seen.

Auto Wiper Control

A continuously working wiper is a big nuisance when it is not raining hard. The wiper control show in Figure 5.4 allows the wiper to sweep at rates varying from once a second to once in 10 seconds.

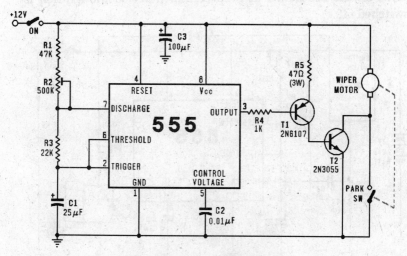

Figure 5.4: Auto wiper cycle timer.

Basically the circuit is an astable multivibrator, (see Figure 4.2) in which the output level at pin 3 remains high for a long time decided by R1+R2, and low for a short time decided by R3. The low going output at output pin 3 drives the wiper motor via T1 and T2 for a time just sufficient to operate the parking switch. The wipers then make one sweep and rest again in their normal parked position till the next pulse. Resistor R5 limits the current and power dissipation in T1. Transistors T1 and T2 should have current handling capability of the wiper motor. They may be replaced by a relay if desired.

Automatic Headlights Turn-Off

Any one who has stumbled around in a dark garage after leaving his car for the night will appreciate this automatic headlight ut off switch. The switch, when installed in a car automatically turns off the headlights at predetermined period the ignition is switched off.

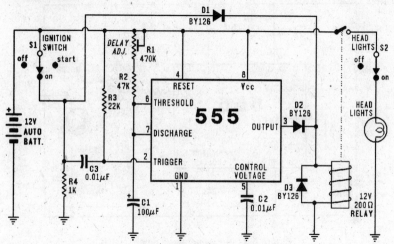

Figure 5.5: Automatic headlights turn off.

In Figure 5.5, when the ignition is first switched on, the battery voltage is fed to the relay coil through diode D1. Switching off the ignition generates a negative-going pulse on pin 2 that triggers the timer. The output of IC goes high to energies the relay and keep the headlights on long enough for you to leave the garage. With the values shown the delay is adjustable from approx. 10 seconds to 1 minute.

Tiny Flasher

A small size LED flasher operating on self contained batteries may be useful as a flashing metronome, dark room timer, memo reminder and other similar applications.

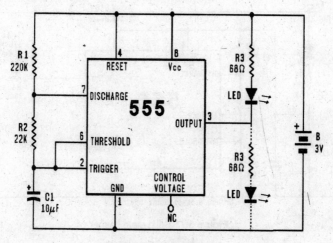

Figure 5.6: LED Flasher.

The circuit of Figure 5.6 is basically an astable multivibrator (see Figure 4.2) with a duty cycle of about 10%. LED connected as shown in Figure 5.6 will be on for a short period and off for a longer period.

The duty cycle will be reversed if R3 and the LED are connected as shown dotted in the Figure. That means that the LED will remain lit for a longer period than the period for which it is off. Battery consumption will also increase accordingly.

Solid State Flasher

The mains operated flasher shown in Figure 5.7 uses a 555 timer to control the ON and OFF times of a triac which controls power to the load.

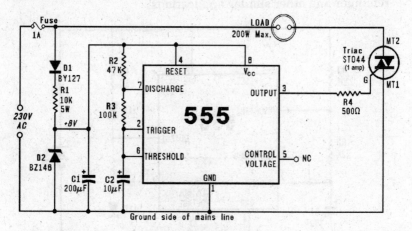

Figure 5.7: Solid-state flasher.

This flasher is also an astable multivibrator circuit (see Figure 4.2) operated on a low voltage dc supply derived from the mains.

The power supply for the IC is obtained by half wave rectifier D1 and a voltage stabilizer circuit comprising a zener diode D2, voltage dropping resistor R1 and filter capacitor C1. This is because the 555 is a low voltage operated IC. A triac of 1A current capacity is used to switch the load on and off.

The lamp in the load circuit remains on for about 1 second and off for about 0.7 seconds. Other timings may be obtained by choosing appropriate values for R2, and R3.

Sense-of-Time Tester

How accurate is your sense of time? You can find it out for your-self by catching a flashing LED.

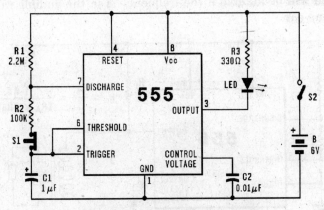

Figure 5.8: Sense of time tester.

When S2 is on, the circuit in Fig 5.8 operates as an astable multivibrator (see Figure 4.2) in which the LED flashes every 1.5 seconds. The LED is lit for about 0.1 second only. Since the human reaction time is more then this, you cannot catch it once it is seen on, by pressing S1. If your sense of time interval is good, and you press S1 within that 0.1 sec., the discharging of C1 stops and then the lamp stays lit. You may change the ON and OFF periods by changing R1 and R2 or C1 to suit your convenience.

This circuit can be a great fun at parties.

Audio Oscillator

If the output of an oscillator is connected to a speaker either through a transformer as shown in Figure 5.9, or by a capacitor, a sound will be audible if the frequency is in the audible range of human ear.

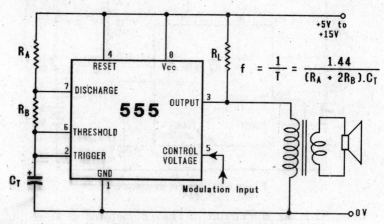

$$f = \frac{1}{T} = \frac{1.44}{(R_A + 2R_B).C_T}$$

Figure 5.9: A simple audio oscillator.

The circuit layout of this oscillator resembles the circuit shown in Figure 4.2. If R_B is made very small, the output will be very sharp pulses. Though they contain a lot of energy, they are not audible because the loudspeaker is silent for a major part of the cycle. As R_B is increased, the pulses generated get wider and that makes them more loud. The sound generated is rich in harmonics and can form a basis to design a simple organ with seven or 13 notes by choosing appropriate values of resistors, switched by keys of the organ or by the touch of a fly lead..

Square Wave Generator

A square wave generator using two resistors was shown in Figure 4.5. With only one external resistor and one capacitor a 555 timer IC can be connected to generate fairly accurate square waves.

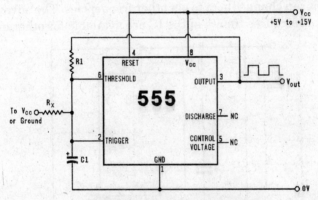

Figure 5.10: Square wave generator.

The square wave generator circuit shown in Figure 5.10 makes use of the fact that output voltage in a 555 IC is 180 degrees out of phase with the voltage across the timing capacitor. To understand the circuit operation let us assume a state when output is high and the capacitor C1 is charging via R1. When the voltage across capacitor reaches $2/3$ V_{cc}, the output goes low and C1 starts discharging through R1. When the voltage across C1 falls to $1/3$ V_{cc} the circuit changes over again. The output goes high, the timing capacitor starts charging and the cycle repeats endlessly.

Since charging the discharging takes through R1 only, the output is a symmetrical square wave. The period of oscillation is given by the expression: T=1.4R1C1. The output symmetry depends on the accuracy of the timer's internal resistor string. These errors can be eliminated by adding a trimming resistor R_X connecting it to supply line or to ground depending on the correction needed.

Square Wave Oscillator

A single section of the Quad timer 558 can be used to make a non-precision oscillator as shown in Figure 5.11. The values of components shown in this Figure are for oscillations at about 400 Hz. You can change them to get other frequencies. The advantage is that other three timers in the IC are available for other uses.

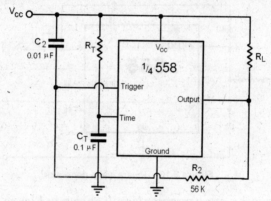

Figure 5.11: Non-precision oscillator.

The principle of working of this circuit is same as that of Figure 5.8 in which the output is fed back to the input.

In this case, $T1 = R_T C_T$ and $T2 = R2C2$ for $V_{cc} = 15$ Volts. The frequency of oscillation is subject to change with changes in V_{cc}.

Linear Saw Tooth Generator

Sawtooth waveforms resemble the shape of teeth of a wood cutting saw. When reproduced as a sound, the tone is rich in harmonics. Linear sawtooth waves are used as time bases for oscilloscopes.

The voltage across the timing capacitor C_T in the monostable multivibrator circuit of Figure 4.1 rises to $2/3$ V_{cc}, and then drops quickly to almost zero. A sawtooth waveform is, therefore, available across this capacitor, but it is not linear because the voltage across the capacitor rises exponentially (see Figure 2.5).

If the capacitor is charged through a constant current source (see Figure 2.11), this voltage will rise linearly.

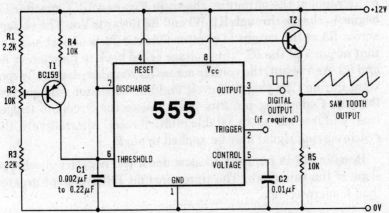

Figure 5.12: Sawtooth generator using a current source.

In Figure 5.12, the capacitor is allowed to charge via a constant current source (see Figure 2.11) comprising of T1, R1, R2, R3 and R4. The voltage now rises linearly. The output is taken via an emitter follower buffer stage T2 to isolate the load from timing circuit. For use as a scope time base, a trigger signal may be applied to terminal 2 or the IC. The frequency of the sawtooth wave can be varied by potentiometer R2.

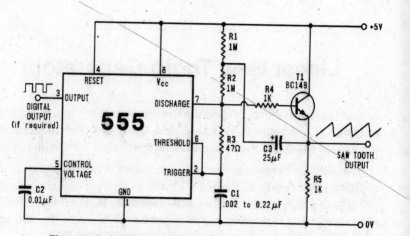

Figure 5.13: Linear sawtooth generator using a bootstrap circuit.

Another arrangement to generate a linear sawtooth can is by bootstrapping the output as shown in Figure 5.13. Capacitor C1 begins to charge through R1, R2 and R3 towards Vcc. The voltage across R5 at the output of emitter follower T1 is almost same as that at pin 7 of the IC. This voltage is fed back to junction of R1 and R2. As a result, the voltage across R2 remains essentially constant during C1's charging cycle and the capacitor voltage rises linearly. Connecting pin 2 to pin 6 causes the circuit to trigger itself and free run as an astable multivibrator. Alternatively, the synchronizing signal may be applied to pin 2.

Resistor R3 is required to slow down the negative discharge slope of the saw tooth. The time constant R3C1 is kept greater than 5 microseconds.

Warble Tone Generator

The tone generator described here is an audio tone generator to attract attention. Such circuits may be used for alarm sirens or for producing unique tones in cable testing. Such tones will not get mixed up with other noises.

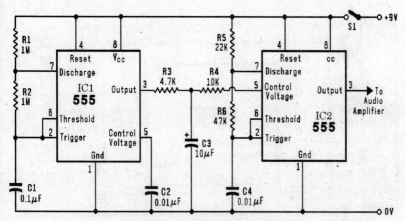

Figure 5.14: Warble tone generator.

In the schematic shown in Figure 5.14, the first 555 timer (IC1) oscillates below 10 Hz. Its square output is filtered by filter R3, R4 and C3 to produce triangular waves. Timer IC2 is used as a 1kHz oscillator which is modulated by the 10 Hz triangular waves from IC1. The exact frequency, rate and deviation of the circuit can be easily modified to produce almost any type of warble sound.

For low power applications, the output can be applied to a speaker via an output transformer, or directly through an isolating capacitor. For louder sounds, the output may be amplified by an audio amplifier to the required power level.

Delayed Automatic Power Off

This circuit will automatically turn off power to your stereo player or radio after about 20 minutes. You can also use such circuits to put off porch light after you lock the house and move out and similar other uses.

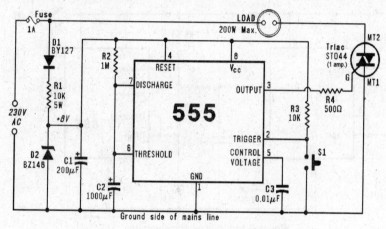

Figure 5.15: Circuit turns off power after a delay.

In Figure 5.15, the 555 timer its operated as a monostable (see Figure 4.1). A momentary push on S1 makes the output go high which triggers the triac and makes power available in the socket. The IC output goes low again when C2 has charged up to 2/3 of the supply voltage which, because of large value of C2 takes about 20 minutes. Capacitor C2 should have low leakage otherwise it will charge very slowly and in case of excessive leakages it may not charge to full value at all. Power supply for the timer is provided by half wave rectifier D1, voltage dropping resistor R1, zener diode D2 and filter capacitor C1.

Delayed Automatic Power On

The circuit shown in Figure 5.16 will turn power ON to the load after a pre-determined delay, about 10 seconds in this case. It might be used to delay the application of power to a fuel pump or start the blower of an air-conditioner before starting the compressor, and similar applications.

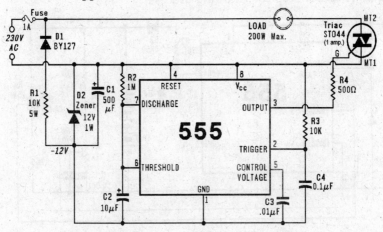

Figure 5.16: Circuit turns power on after a delay.

The circuit again uses a triac as in Figure 5.15 and utilizes the fact that a triac can be switched on by a negative bias also. Here, capacitor C2 starts charging from the instant the plug is put into power socket.

When capacitor C2 is charged to $2/3\ V_{cc}$ the output goes low and the negative voltage triggers the triac energizing the load.

Ni-Cd Battery Charger

The battery charger shown in Figure 5.17 maintains a full charge on a standby supply for an instrument that is always connected to the ac power line, whether in use or not. The two comparators of the IC 555 are used in this application to monitor the battery voltage and start or stop the charging process.

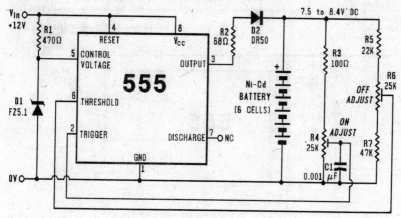

Figure 5.17: Ni-Cd Battery charger.

Zener diode D1 provides a reference voltage for both comparators through the timer's internal resistive voltage divider chain (see Figure 3.2). The charge ON and the charge OFF points are adjusted by independent potentiometers R4 and R6. Resistor R2 prevents the charging current exceeding 150 mA under all conditions. Diode D2 prevents discharging of the battery through the timer when its output is in low state.

To calibrate the timer, substitute the Ni-Cd batteries by a variable voltage dc power supply and set the ON, and OFF potentiometers to work at the desired voltages. Monitor voltage at output pin 3 to see when the output goes on or off.

Wide Range Pulse Generator

Pulse generators deliver a pulse of known pulse width (duration) when required, or at repeatedly ad a prespecified rate. Such generators are used for testing digital circuits. The general purpose pulse generator described here provides a wide range of frequencies in decade ranges and independent control of pulse width and frequency.

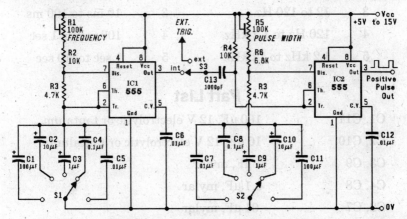

Figure 5.18: Wide range pulse generator.

In Figure 5.18, the first timer IC1 is used as an astable multivibrator (see Figure 4.2) whose pulse rate (frequency) can be varied over a 10:1 range by potentiometer R1. Range selection is done by a 5-position switch S1. Thus, the total range covered is from 0.12 Hz to 12 kHz. Mylar capacitors will provide stability of calibration on higher ranges. Tantalum capacitors are recommended for the same reason for low pulse rates.

The second timer IC2 is used as a monostable (see Figure 4.1) whose output is a pulse having a width that can be varied over a range of 10:1 by R5. Selection switch S2 provides five ranges of pulse width from 100 micro-seconds to 10 seconds.

The output of first timer IC1 is fed to the trigger input of the second timer IC2 via S3. This switch also has a position in which IC2 can be triggered by an external signal, if desired. In external mode, any negative going pulse can be used to trigger the circuit.

When triggered, IC2 delivers a positive going pulse. The following tables give the ranges of frequency and pulse width.

Position of S1	Frequency range	Position of S2	Pulse width
1	0.12 to 1.2 Hz	1	100 µs to 1 ms
2	1.2 to 12 Hz	2	1 ms to 10 ms
3	12 to 120 Hz	3	10 ms to 100 ms
4	120 Hz to 1.2 kHz	4	100 ms to 1 sec
5	1.2 kHz to 12 kHz	5	1 sec to 10 sec

Part List

C1, C11	100 µF, 12 V electrolytic or tantalum
C2, C10	10 µF, 12 V electrolytic or tantalum.
C3, C9	1 µF, mylar
C4, C8	0.1 µF, mylar
C2, C7	.01 µF, mylar
C6, C12	.01 µF, ceramic
C13	.01 µF, mylar
R1, R5	100 kΩ potentiometer
R2	10 kΩ, ¼ W
R3	4.7 kΩ, ¼ W
R4	10 kΩ, ¼ W
R6	6.8 kΩ, ¼ W
S1, S2	Two pole 5-way switch
S3	Single pole two way switch
Timer	555 IC 2 Nos.

A Simple Tone Burst generator

A very simple tone burst generator circuit using a 555 Timer is shown in Figure 5.19. It delivers a train of square waves whenever the push button switch is tapped.

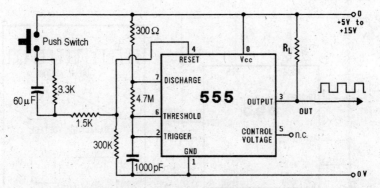

Figure 5.19: A simple tone burst generator.

A 555 timer IC is used as a square wave generator. This circuit resembles the circuit of Figure 4.5. However, in this case the square wave generator is triggered by a positive going trigger pulse applied to its Reset terminal.

The Reset terminal is normally kept connected to ground via a 300 k ohms resistor. A push on the push button switch generates a short positive going pulse, making the Reset terminal high for a short period. During this time interval, the square wave output generated by 555 is available at the output.

Frequency Divider

The IC timer 555 can be used to divide a known frequency by adjusting the length of the timing cycle. This application makes use of the fact that a 555 timer cannot be retriggered during the timing cycle.

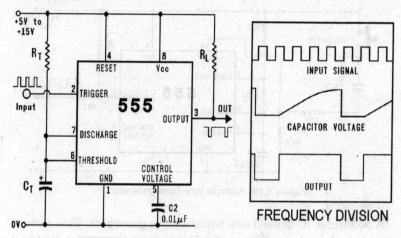

Figure 5.20: Frequency divider.

Figure 5.20 shows the external hook-up as well as the waveforms for a divide-by-five circuit. The frequency to be divided is applied to trigger input (pin No. 2). The negative edge of the applied signal triggers the timer and capacitor C_T starts charging. During the charging process, further incoming pulses have no effect. The capacitor charges to its threshold value. Now, when the circuit is triggered, capacitor C_T discharges and circuit waits in this position to be triggered by next pulse. If R_T and C_T are chosen properly, the circuit can be made to trigger on second, third, fourth or more pulses and the output will be a frequency equal to the input frequency divided by that number. This working is explained by the waveforms in Figure 5.20.

Missing Pulse Detector

A 555 timer connected as shown in Figure 5.21 can detect a missing pulse or abnormally long period between two consecutive pulses in a train of pulses. Such circuits can be used to detect intermittent firing of a spark plug in an internal combustion engine or to monitor the heart beat of a sick patient.

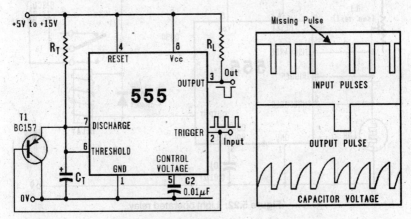

Figure 5.21 Missing pulse detector.

The signal from the pick-up transducer is shaped to form a negative going pulse and is applied to pin 2 of the IC which is connected as a monostable. As long as the spacing between the pulse is less than the timing interval, the timing cycle is continuously reset by the input pulses and the capacitor is discharged via T1. A decrease in pulse frequency or a missing pulse permits completion of time interval which causes a change in the output level. Wave forms in this operation are also shown in Figure 5.21.

Light Operated Relay

A light dependent resistor (LDR) can be used with a 555 timer to form a photo sensitive relay in an intruder alarm system or for switching on a light at sun set and switch it off at sun rise.

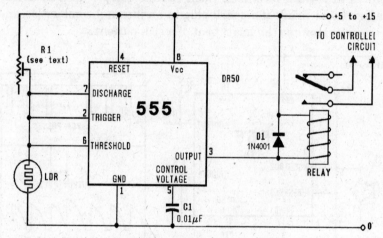

Figure 5.22: Light operated relay.

Resistor R1 in Figure 6.22 is so adjusted that under normal conditions when the light is falling on the photo-cell, the voltage across the photo-cell is less than $1/3$ V_{cc}. The actual value of R1 will depend on the resistance of the LDR. The output in this condition is high and the relay is off.

As the day-light fades or the light on the LDR is interrupted by an intruder, the voltage across it rises above $2/3$ V_{cc}, tripping the IC flip flop. The output goes low actuating the relay. When the light is restored, the voltage falls below $1/3$ V_{cc} again tripping the flip-flop causing the output go high and the relay drops. The difference between turning on and turning off voltages, which is equal to $1/3$ V_{cc} prevents relay chatter.

DC-to-DC Converter

Many circuits, especially digital circuits, need dc power supplies at different voltages. Such a supplies can be made easily by using a 555 timer as a square wave generator of high frequency.

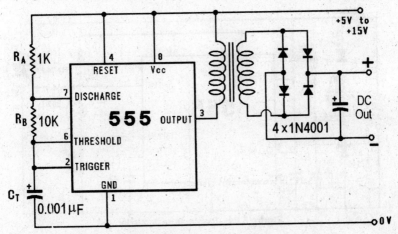

Figure 5.23: DC-to-DC converter.

.The square wave generator circuit shown in Figure 5.23 resembles the square wave oscillator shown in Figure 4.5. The high frequency output is stepped up (or down) by a transformer, converted into pulsating dc by a bridge rectifier. The capacitor in the output filters the ripples and supplies a steady dc voltage needed by the other circuit.

Temperature Controller

A 555 timer can be used with a thermistor resistor divider to build a temperature controller. The advantage offered is that a well regulated supply is not required.

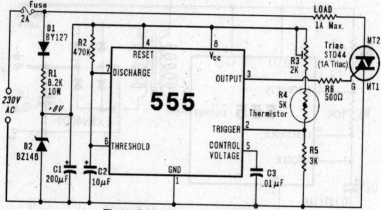

Figure 5.24: Temperature controller.

The dividing network in Figure 5.24 consists of an adjustable resistance R3, thermistor R4 and fixed resistor R5. When thermistor R4 cools below a set value the voltage at pin 2 of the 555 drops below $1/3\,V_{cc}$. This makes the output go high and that turns on the triac controlled heater and also starts the timing cycle. If the thermistor temperature rises above the set point before the end of the timing cycle the heater shuts off at the end of the timing period. Otherwise the heater continues to stay on.

Thermistors of different values can be used as long as R3+R4 = 2R5 holds true at the desired temperature.

Brightness Control of LED Displays

The visible brightness of a light emitting diode or seven segment LED type displays can be continuously varied by applying a pulsed signal and varying its duty cycle. Seven-segment decoders usually have a Blanking Input terminal where this type of control can be applied. If the frequency of the pulsed signal is above 50 Hz, the flicker will not be noticeable.

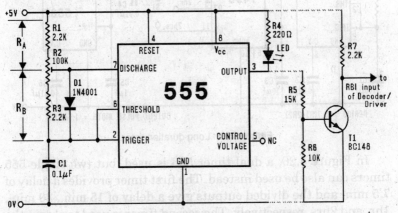

Figure 5.25: Brightness control of LED displays.

In Figure 5.25 the charge and discharge times of the timing capacitor C1 vary with the setting of potentiometer R2 but the total period remains the same. Thus the output signal frequency remains unaffected while its duty cycle is varied over a wide range. The output controls the brightness of LEDs.

For applying to the ripple-blanking input of decoder(s), a booster transistor may be connected as shown on the right side to provide sufficient drive voltage and power.

Long Duration Timer

The 555 timer teamed up with a [1]binary divider can provide delays as much as sixteen times of that set by the time constant of the first timer.

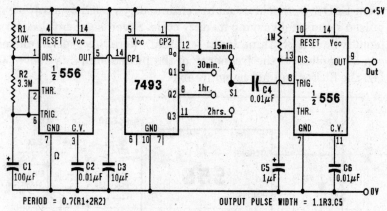

Figure 5.26: Long duration timer.

In Figure 5.26, a dual timer 556 is used, but two single 555 timers can also be used instead. The first timer provides a delay of 7.5 min. and the divided outputs give a delay of 15 min., 30 min., 1hr. and 2hrs. respectively. The second timer is used to obtain the desired output pulse length. Additional dividers may be added to give longer delays.

---

[1] Digital dividers and other digital integrated circuits are described in author's book Learning by Experiments — Digital Integrated Circuits, which is published by BPB Publications.

The digital version of 555 timer has internal built-in circuitry for dividing etc. functions and it can directly be used for long delay applications. It is described in author's book Electronic Timers and Practical Applications, published by BPB Publications.

Sequential Switching

Several timers can be connected in cascade to control a number
of operations in a sequential manner. Such circuits are useful in
automatic control or automatic testing or sequential operation of
machines. The on-time of each machine can be set independently.

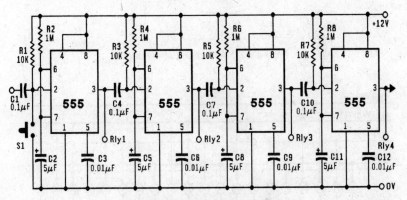

Figure 5.27: Sequential switching.

When the power is switched on in Figure 5.27, all timers are in
off state (output low). Pressing the start button S1 momentarily
triggers the first timer and its output goes high. After the time
interval (1.1 R2 C2) its output again goes low, triggering the next
timer and so on.

It is possible to connect the output of the last timer back to the
first timer to trigger it. The action in this case once started by S1
will keep on repeating endlessly. The four timers shown in Figure
5.26 can be used to control four relays which will switch in a se-
quence 1,2,3,4,1,2, ... Such sequential switching with equal time
interval can be used to switch decorative lights or advertising displays. Two examples of connections, one which produces an illu-
sion of a revolving wheel and the other that of a running border
are shown in Figures 5.28 and 5.29 respectively.

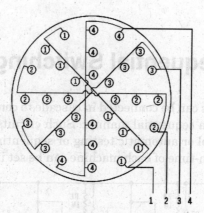

Figure 5.28: A revolving wheel display.

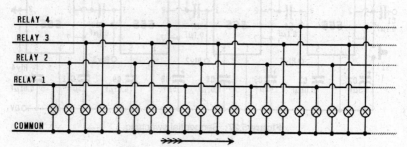

Figure 5.29: A running lights display.

Appendix A

Ratings and Characteristics

It is easy to design reliably performing electronic cirucits if you know the characteristics and limits of an integrated circuit before you design a circuit. This kind of information is given in this Appendix.

Absolute Maximum Ratings

Parameter	Rating	Unit

Supply voltage
  SE555
  NE555, SE555C
	+18
	+16
		V
		V

Power dissipation	600	mW

Operating temperature range
  SE555
  NE555, SE555C
	0 to +70
	-55 to +125
		°C
		°C

Storage temperature range	-65 to 150	°C
Lead temperature (soldering (60s)	+300	°C

Parameter	Rating	Unit

Supply voltage
  NE/SA558
  SE558
	+16
	+18
		V
		V

Power dissipation	1.35	W

Operating temperature range
  NE558
  SE558
	0 to +70
	-55 to +125
		°C
		°C

Storage temperature range	-65 to 150	°C
Lead temperature (soldering (60s)	+300	°C

555/7555/TLC555

		555			7555			TLC555			Unit
		Min.	Typ.	Max.	Min	Typ.	Max.	Min.	Typ.	Max.	
Vcc/Vdd		4.5		18	2		18	2		18	V
Supply current	2V		-	-	-		-		-	0.25	mA
	5V		3	5	0.08		0.4		0.170.-	0.35	mA
	10V		10	12	0.12		0.6		36	0.60	mA
Output current	Isink		200		8		80		100		mA
	Isource		200		1		20		10		mA
Threshold current			100	200			10		0.01		nA
Discharge state-off current			20	100			10		0.1		nA
MMV timing error			1	3		2			1	3	%
Temp. drift				500		250			-	-	ppm/
Vcc drift output				0.5		0.3	1		0.1	0.5	%/V
rise-time			100	300		75			20		nS
fall-time			100	300		75			75		nS
fmax				0.5		1			2		MHz

Index

Symbols

555 testing 44
555 Timers 21
556 dual timer 30
558 quad timer 30, 41

A

analog 2
astable 36, 41

B

bistable 39

C

capacitor
  charging linear 13
  charging of 5
  charging at con-
    stant current 10
  discharging 7
  leakage, effect of 9
  tantalum 10
clock, grandfather 1
clock, wall 1
comparators 14
constant current
  sources 11
control terminal 28
control voltage 32

D

devices
  analog 2
  digital 2
digital integrated
    circuits 70

E

exponential curves 10

F

flip-flop 24

G

grandfather clock 1

H

Hysteresis 16

L

load, feeding it 25
Load, inductive, 18

M

monostable 35, 41

N

Ni-Cd battery charger
  60

O

op amp 15
output 31
output surge 29
outputs totem pole 19

P

Photo Timer 45
Power Supplies 20
Practical Applications
  43

Q

Quad Timer 558 41

R

Relay
  driving it 26
Reset 32
Resetting 27

S

sand clock 3
Schmitt Trigger 40
sink current 17
source current 17
square wave oscillator
  38, 54

T

tau (τ) 6
Time Measurement 1
time constant 6
time piece alarm 2
time up indicators 17
timer
  555, digital 70
  basic circuit 14
  CMOS 7555 32
  dual, 556 30
  electro-mech. 5
  long duration 70
  mechanical 4
  photo 45
  quad, 558, 30, 41
  sand clock 3
  testing 44
timers 3
  555 family 21
  analog 5
  operation of 35
  pin connections 22
totem pole outputs 19
triggering 27, 28

W

wall clock 1
watch, pocket 2
watch, wrist 2

By the Same Author:-

41 Projects using 741 Op Amp
51 Projects using CD4011
Batteries, Chargers and Emergency Lights
Build Your Own Disco Projects
Build Your Own Test Instruments
CMOS Integrated Circuits–Learning by Experiments
CorelDRAW Graphics Suite X3 Training Guide
CorelDRAW Graphics Suite X4 Training Guide
Designing Coils and Transformers
Desk Top Publishing on PC
Digital Integrated Circuits–Learning by Experiments
Easy to Build Electronic Alarms
Electronic Formulas, Tables and Symbols
Electronic Timers and Practical Applications
Fast Servicing with Modern Multimeters
Fast Servicing with Oscilloscopes
Flash CS4 (version 11) Training Guide
Function Generators and Phase Lock Loops
Music and Sound ICs and Circuits
Op Amps Made Simple
Photoshop CS5 Training Guide
Practical Electronic Power Supplies
Practical SCR and Triac Projects
Simple Audio Projects
The Little Book on Computers
Voltage Stabilizers and Automatic Cutouts
Voltage Stabilizers and Automatic Cutouts (in Hindi)
Computer - Ek Purna Parichay (in Hindi) Winner of First Prize by
All India Council for Technical Education, Government of India.
Desk Top Publishing on PC (in Hindi). Winner of Bhartendu
Harischandra *Man Puraskar*, Ministry of Information and
Technology, Government of India.